Fangtastic Rhymes

Edited By Megan Roberts

First published in Great Britain in 2020 by:

YoungWriters®
Est. 1991

Young Writers
Remus House
Coltsfoot Drive
Peterborough
PE2 9BF
Telephone: 01733 890066
Website: www.youngwriters.co.uk

Printed and bound in the UK by BookPrintingUK
Website: www.bookprintinguk.com
YB0433C

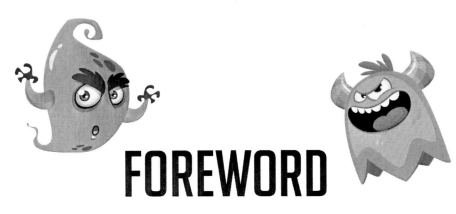

FOREWORD

Hello Reader!

For our latest poetry competition we sent out funky and vibrant worksheets for primary school pupils to fill in and create their very own poem about fiendish fiends and crazy creatures. I got to read them and guess what? They were **roarsome**!

The pupils were able to read our example poems and use the fun-filled free resources to help bring their imaginations to life, and the result is pages **oozing** with exciting poetic tales. From friendly monsters to mean monsters, from bumps in the night to **rip-roaring** adventures, these pupils have excelled themselves, and now have the joy of seeing their work in print!

Here at Young Writers we love nothing more than poetry and creativity. We aim to encourage children to put pen to paper to inspire a love of the written word and explore their own unique worlds of creativity. We'd like to congratulate all of the aspiring authors that have created this book of **monstrous mayhem** and we know that these poems will be enjoyed for years to come. So, dive on in and submerge yourself in all things furry and fearsome (and perhaps check under the bed!).

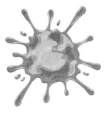

CONTENTS

Sacriston Primary School, Sacriston

Jacob Key (7)	63
Warren Albert Rowbury (7)	64
Ryan Pallister (7)	65
Harvey Berry (7)	66
Oliver David Winn (7)	67
Thomas Davidson (8)	68
Jaydan James Musgrove (7)	69
Charlie Atkinson (7)	70

St Bernadette's RC Primary School, Whitefield

Hannah Miller (7)	71
Oscar Morton (8)	72
Jack Barrow (7)	74
Jessica B (8)	75
Louis O'Donnell (8)	76
Zak Wegg (8)	77
Gracie B (8)	78
Luke Ryan (8)	79
George Badlan (8)	80
James Simpson (7)	81
Ethan Brower (8)	82
Freddie Mollard (8)	83
Tom Dalton (8)	84
Donatas S (8)	85
Grace Hadman (9)	86
Mia Rose Williams (7)	87
Martha Lily Tait (7)	88
Freya Linaker (7)	89
Madeleine Ohamara (7)	90
Luca Bailey (8)	91
Charlie N (8)	92
Daniel Yusuf Patelmama (9)	93
Ella F (8)	94
Charlotte May Griffiths (8)	95
Erin Katie Eckersley (8)	96
Zack Cooper-Gibb (8)	97
Isabella Jane Jones (7)	98
Heidi Betty Mullen (8)	99
Nell Redmond (8)	100

Shannon Costello (7)	101
James K (8)	102
Theo H (8)	103
Cole Green (9)	104
Finley Mountford (8)	105
Aidan Lewis (8)	106
Robert Zakrzewski (8)	107
Grace Emily Weber (8)	108
Harry Marshall (7)	109
Zak Zain Crampton (8)	110
Teddy Langston C (8)	111
Callum John Kirby (7)	112
Ronnie Knowles (8)	113
Thomas Hugh Colohan (8)	114
Aidan Simmonds (8)	115
Sam Hopkins (7)	116
Ciaran Howe (8)	117
Stella Chan (8)	118
Maximilian Holt (7)	119
Olivia W (8)	120
Ryan Firth (8)	121
Kian F (8)	122
Keane Forshaw (8)	123
Aven James Wallsworth (7)	124
Leo	125

St Mary's CE (VC) J&I School, Sowerby Bridge

Archie Sinclair Willis (10)	126
Arron Lapsley (10)	128
Lily Reynolds Norman (10)	130
Lucia Filomena Wilson Pignataro (10)	131
Arthur Beddoe (10)	132
Maia Wood (10)	133
Jude Blackburn (10)	134
Molly Ledger (10)	136
Beck Jameson (10)	138
Chloe Davies (10)	140
Anna Louise Walker (10)	141
Ayla Amos (11)	142
Holly Jaime O'Connor (11)	143

St Patrick's Primary School, Glasgow

Eshan Kabuye (10)	144
Dominykas Dankis (10)	146
Hassan Ali Bhatti (9)	147
Sophie Chanelle McKay (10)	148
Mehmet Ali Kocoglu (10)	149
Baillie Hutchison (9)	150
Lenka Malgorzata (10)	151
Maci McCusker (10)	152

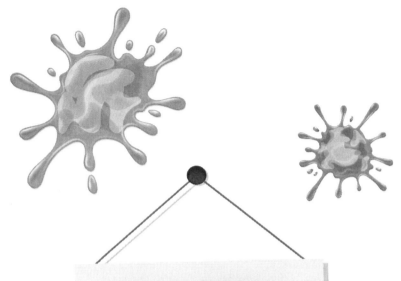

THE POEMS

Lilith The Demon

She was flying through the street
When I heard her make a peep
Then I turned around and noticed her
She was smaller than a fig
Pink as a pig
Then I asked her name, it was Lilith
She was as fluffy as a bunny
She was also really funny
And her wings were just like bats
Her third eye opened up
And she's quite scared of pups
But that doesn't stop her having fun
She had yellow and black horns that shoot out sparks
She had sparky powers in hands, *pow! Pow!*
She had a vibrant, pink bow
And then she flew down low
Zoom! Zoom! off she goes
Loving Lilith with a bright purple heart on her chest
Zoom! Zoom!
Did I mention she was small?

Mirren Jane Wallace (10)
Bramble Brae School, Aberdeen

Monster

Fluffy was walking down the jungle path
And no one went past
He was scared and frightened
But he would last
He saw his cave glowing in the distance
It was nothing, it was just his imagination
He walked and walked until he found his cave
And then the sky went *poof*
Then the day began
When Fluffy walked into the cave
He saw a monster waving

Remember Fluffy was only 3.5ft
He looked like a Tic Tac
His elegant eyes were shining
He was fluffy and chubby
He ran and ran until he found a cave
It was dark and scary but he thought it was safe
He sat down and exhaled
He heard a grunt
He did not know if it was him or his tum
He grunted back

And followed the sound
He found his replica in the dark
He gasped for air from running too much
He looked left and right
He looked in front
Boom!
His replica was right in front of him
Nom! Nom! Nom!

Katie Lavinia Taylor (10)
Bramble Brae School, Aberdeen

Mix Mash

Mix Mash is like a living machine
With a microwave for a head
He has a crocodile for an arm
And its name is Chomps

An iceberg for the other leg
But at football, he always gets megged
A bookshelf for a chest
And a truck for the left arm with metal plates

With all this, he is as slow as a slug
But around half-past five, he goes *ping* for tea
He's read all the books in his big bookshelf
But it's alright to read them twice
He's powered by potatoes
But he does not like his tomatoes

He lives in a hut with a bunch of bananas
His hut is on a bay on an uncharted island with a
tiki bar
The island is quite small
Because he is a bit tall

But he's not a machine
He's not an animal
He is a monster!

Callum

Bramble Brae School, Aberdeen

Stary

Stary, our teacher, shape-shifted into a cat
Spotty all over, fluffy as a lion's neck
Stary flies some of the time, he shifted into a mat
His bed is a flowerpot on a windowsill

Stary is as lazy as a pig
Stary runs two miles a day
Stary says hi to a wig
Stary tells you weird puns

He likes to eat children and adults for lunch
He takes their head off and put it in a bin!
He likes to eat children for breakfast
He likes girls to marry him

If you tickle him, he goes 'hehe'
He tells everyone that he
Is as fluffy as a hairball
It rolls all over the floor

Stary's beady eyes are crazy
As a buffalo, he laughs at you all day

You tickle his tummy, he tickles his butt
Checks he likes to rhyme at me all day.

Charlie Mcmillan (10)
Bramble Brae School, Aberdeen

Fizzy The Monster

F erociously hungry and fluffy like a dog
I ncredible like an insect
Z ooms, zooms, zooms like a car
Fi **Z** zes like fizzy juice
Y uck like a duck and yellow as the sun

T ired like dogs, tiny like ants
H as sharp horns, hates hats
E xcited when sees cake, hates exercise

M eets a mouse, likes monkeys
O reos are hated, plays Noggle
N ever naughty
S ticky like sweets
T ries to be nice, she hates sticky toffee pudding
E ven likes elephants, hates earrings
R espects others and friendly.

Callie
Bramble Brae School, Aberdeen

Monster Poem

Slime has pink eyes
Bright as the bright blue sky
Slime's hair spikes up very tall
Slime likes his jet-black hair
He has polka dots on his nose and tummy
His favourite colours are neon bright
I don't know why!
He is sweet and kind
His ears are big and they have piercings on them
His piercings are as silver as a mirror
His teeth are very white
His eyes are big bright and beautiful
As light as the sunrise
He likes to stroll in the park
When he walks, his feet thump
It makes a bang every time his feet move
He loves playing on the swings
He screams, "Argh!"

Kimberly Stewart
Bramble Brae School, Aberdeen

Unown

This monster is small
It's mostly found in caves
And walking down the halls
Mostly just to wave.

It's very small and weak
But it could fly so high
However, you don't know
Where it could be
It can fly so high it reaches Cloud Nine.

When you are scared in the middle of nowhere
Then that means Unown is there.

But don't worry, he is quite friendly so don't be
afraid.

Theo Michael Wilson (10)
Bramble Brae School, Aberdeen

Creepy The Creeper

Creepy the creeper
Is as explosive as TNT
He goes *sssss... bang*
When he explodes
But he is friendly
Only to my best friends though
You wait to eat bacon when he is hungry
But if you make him mad
He will explode
He likes to play Minecraft and Roblox with you
And when he goes to bed, it's really
Quite peaceful too
And when he wakes up, he likes to eat explosive
eves.

Hamish Dylan Henderson (10)
Bramble Brae School, Aberdeen

The Midnight Monster...

In the dark, dark caves of Caralafia lies a furious
monster beast.
Its eyes were dark as a black hole.
Its body was scaly like spikes.
Its teeth were sharper than steel.
Its body was red.
Like no one has ever said!
He never steals a deal.
His name was Shape-Shifter Swirly.
He eats like a never-fed zombie.
He goes *zoom!* Like a boom.
He has more stitches than spikes.

Christopher Henderson
Bramble Brae School, Aberdeen

Monster

He has scaly, vibrant skin
With a spiky, glowing back
He has a sharp, silly, shiny mohawk
Teeth as blue as Blu Tack

Zig and zoom, off he goes
On his toes
Riding off in rows

He wraps people in cocoons
And he sees loads of moons
He thinks they're fools
And loves to jump in pools

As hungry as a ferocious lion
And he knows when you're lying.

Rhylan Stuart Quinn (10)
Bramble Brae School, Aberdeen

Kobra

Kylo is as short as a bucket
His nose is as orange as an orange plug
He slides across the room like a slug
Sksksksksksksksksksksksksksksksk

He has a pet dinosaur
That eats Peppa Pig and a rusk
He has sharp, pointy ears
With lots of earrings

Three blue eyes
Red hair like ruby rings

Kylo is the best monster ever.

James Thomas Miller (10)
Bramble Brae School, Aberdeen

Monster

"Hi, my name is Tofik the Teddy
I like to fly high in the garden
I like to cuddle everybody
I am very fluffy!"
Tofik likes to sleep on the fluffy bed
Tofik likes to play in the deep deep snow like a
pool
When he walks he makes a noise: sssssss.

Hanna Adrykowska
Bramble Brae School, Aberdeen

Fortnite Monster

He thumps around the Fortnite map
He jumps really high when he sees a Fortnite
character
Don't walk into the monster
He is scary and scaly, don't smile
He will put you in a pile
Of people in his mouth
So watch out
He will eat you like a Brussel sprout.

Reilly
Bramble Brae School, Aberdeen

Starbucks Demon!

As the Starbucks demon
Flies into your room in the midnight sky,
You wake up and wonder what it is,
As it looks down you scream, "Help!"
As it slobbers over you
Strange... Go "Boo!" at the Starbucks Monster
And you turn crazy.

Madison Fraser (9)
Bramble Brae School, Aberdeen

Area 51

A n alien called Area 51
R eally smart and scary
E very day, he goes on a bike ride
A s green as grass

5 1 friends
1 orange bike.

Nathen Gray (10)
Bramble Brae School, Aberdeen

Monsters Camping

If you see monsters camping
They would probably be stamping
But this monster is nice
He eats rice instead of mice
At night, he can see bright
Without a light
All the other monsters hate their brothers
But not this one - Smash
He crashes into walls
He loves to play in a sandpit
One day, Smash was found in a box
Inside, there was a sick fox
Smash wrapped it up
And scratched its head
He put the fox in bed
And fed it every day
Until it ran away.

Keyaan Mahomea (8)
Falconbrook Primary School, Battersea

Oogastella

Me and my dad were taking a stroll
When I heard a sound that echoed around
Then I looked beside me
And it was hideous
So hideous, my eyes fell out
And my mouth dropped
It was like an alien but with strange hair
I was so shocked, I went blind
And then, she said, "Do you wanna play?"
I said, "No! No! No! No!"
Then I was gone in a flash
And left Oogastella behind
That's why I don't have dolls
I only have action figures!

Naima Atchade (8)
Falconbrook Primary School, Battersea

Spark The Monster

One dark night, Spark wanted a shark.
He would always want a mark,
But he did, for going to the park.
Late at night, Spark took a shark to the park.
You would never go near Spark,
Spark likes sharks and dog barks.
He wished he had a dog that barks.
He wished he had a shark, that gives marks.
He would always get a mark, for going to the park.

Leyla Mohamed (8)

Falconbrook Primary School, Battersea

Huge Bum

Hi, I am Huge Bum
I have a huge bum
I am strong
I am brave
I have a huge bum
I do the biggest poop
I get a golden star
That goes on the floor
Now, let's talk about my bum
My name is Huge Bum
Because I have a huge bum
So yay, you got me now
I'm Huge Bum.

Shadda Omar (9)
Falconbrook Primary School, Battersea

Grindor The Monster

There once was a monster called Grindor
He was the toughest monster on the planet
One day, another monster was created
He was stronger than Grindor
One day, he was battling the person
Until two children came and helped him
He said thank you and he was a great monster.

Ayaan Mohammed Siddiqui (8)
Falconbrook Primary School, Battersea

The Hairy Scary Monster

Every night, I hear a growl
From the hairy, scary monster
Waiting to prowl
So I just ignored it
Because I was in doubt
Then I just slept happily.

Uriel Emanuel Ugbaja (8)
Falconbrook Primary School, Battersea

Sweet Sindy

Sweet Sindy, oh sweet Sindy
As cute as a baby but as fierce as a lion
She's a pretty round ball with a long, snake-like
tongue.
Fluffy, spotty fur, terrifying shape-shifter
Giant horns.

When Sindy is hungry, her tummy roars
Like a dinosaur, *roar!*
She makes a lot of noise, as loud as war
The little monster loves sweets
As much as you love your family

The sweet monster is as sneaky as a spy
Sindy goes around the world
Upsetting children by taking all their chocolate
And sweets for Easter and birthdays
And Halloween and Christmas
Naughty monster!

Elif Stamcheva (9)
New Milton Junior School, New Milton

Breakfast Meal Monster

He's frightening, he smells
He's your breakfast meal
The Breakfast Meal Monster
He has sizzling, heating, fried egg eyes
A fluffy, puffy pancake face
Crispy bacon moustache
A gooey, golden, slippery syrup mouth
He drools milk
Leaving a path of white milk
The Breakfast Meal Monster
Has stubby sausage arms
And a waffle, circular body
Toast feet
When he gets angry, his toast feet burn
And go pitch-black
So don't make him angry
He strolls silently with his short, toast feet
He's the king of all breakfasts
He's very breakfasty
Delicious and monstrous
He's frightening

He smells
He's your breakfast meal
The Breakfast Meal Monster
Watch out!

Emma Monserrate (10)

New Milton Junior School, New Milton

The Reluctant Monster

There is a little monster only ten feet tall
Who found being a monster the hardest thing of all
He was shy, forgetful and bumbling
And, when he attempted to shout and scream
He just ended up mumbling

He thinks the reason he's not scary
Is because he's just not hairy
But he hasn't got fangs or needle-sharp claws
Whenever he speaks, he squeaks not roars

He's tried being mean and ever so bad
But it just doesn't work and he simply feels sad
So he's decided to give up this monstering lark
And is busy making friends in the play park.

Catherine Baker (8)
New Milton Junior School, New Milton

The Leader Of The Pugs

I am telling you to hide your pets
Especially pugs
Because the Pug Leader is coming
To collect his children
So hide your pugs and your Uggs
When you hide them, be careful
You may hear bangs on your wall
Or you could be too late
Because the almighty Pug Leader knows all

I faced him once
He smelled disgusting and gross
But it was the most
Also, his face looked scrunched up
And he was taller waist up
Ever since this happened
My poor pug has been gone
I haven't seen him since.

Darcy Courtney (10)
New Milton Junior School, New Milton

Fuzzles, The Friendly Monster

My pet monster is called Fuzzles
He eats carrot soup and guzzles
He is my favourite friend in all the land
We are thinking of starting a rock band
He is good at playing guitar and drums
I will sing very loud while chewing custard
bubblegum
We will be famous all over social media
Just use Google to view our Wikipedia
While Fuzzles practises his drumming skills on my
mum's pots and pans
I practise my pouting for the selfies with all our
fans.

Brooke Angel Parrish (8)
New Milton Junior School, New Milton

Monsterific

Big-headed Brain Dead Man
This is no ordinary man
He moves like a monster
That's 'cause he is

He comes out at night
And gives you a fright
Turns on the light
And giggles

In the background, you hear
"Hahahaha!" again and again
You hope you're in a dream
But you're not

You scream the place down
Running up and down the stairs
And around and around
You'll live.

Lydia Buswell (10)
New Milton Junior School, New Milton

Devil Girl

Night struck, two bright yellow eyes gleamed in the
darkness
Little, pointy, horrendous ears pricked up
Then a mischievous, swaying tail
The devil girl was out and about
She was lurking through the forest
With a cheeky smile on her face
She stalked through the silent, ominous streets
Sneaked through an open window
Scurried upstairs and crept under a bed
Eager to scare someone
A girl woke up... "Boo!"
She screamed.

Hannah Joseph (9)
New Milton Junior School, New Milton

Grimslime

Spooky shadows made their way down the hall
Waiting for a child's call
Gnarled fingernails
Rusty horns
Each monster told a different tale

The scary Grimslime lurked and slithered
Green slime gushed out
His face was scrunched into a pout
He ate up anything in sight
He gave everyone a scary fright

If you see him
Don't worry if you do
Make sure the slime doesn't get on you.

Maisie Wardle (10)
New Milton Junior School, New Milton

My Monster

My monster is big
My monster is scary
He's also a little bit hairy
He's purple and green
And glows in the dark so he can be seen
He has six arms and four pointy ears
He has tiny feet and doesn't smell sweet
With so many arms, he thinks he's funny
And really loves tickling your tummy
His name is Tickly
But he isn't prickly
He's a little bit spotty
And still uses the potty.

Will Graham (7)
New Milton Junior School, New Milton

The Ding In The Tin

There once lived a thing in a tin called Ding
His tummy rumbled so he got in a grumble
Scaring cats, eating bones
Seeing scared faces along the road
Going in bins and getting bones
Licking them up like dominos
Knocking them down and racing them to the end
That's enough for one night
But I think there's room for one more scare
On the way back home
He gets back in the tin and is once again alone.

Izzie Hendy (10)
New Milton Junior School, New Milton

Slimy Simon

I come out in the night
To give people a fright
I'm really scary
Because my eyeballs are hairy
I leave a slime trail
That drips from my tail
I know it makes people mad
But I was born to be bad
In the morning, when you see all the muck
I sit back and pray that you get stuck
Because it's so much fun
When you can't run
I have the best time
When you're stuck in my slime.

Thomas Watson (7)
New Milton Junior School, New Milton

Leo The Purple Monster

Leo is a ball of purple fur
Tickle his tummy and he will purr
He swoops in the dark sky
Flying like a kite
He doesn't like the day
He only flies at night

Leo's always hungry
His favourite food is rocks
But every time I see him
I feed him stinky socks

When he's finished eating
He sleeps in a tree
He really is the best monster
There ever could be!

Scarlett Hitchens (8)
New Milton Junior School, New Milton

Hag Greeny's World

Hag Greeny is brown but not with a frown
His horns are like an orange crown
His bulldozer tail goes *bash! Bash! Bash!*
Then he soars through the sky in a flash, flash, flash
He spins like a devil
Squirts like a squid
Flies like a bird and scares every kid

Hag Greeny is bold with a tale to be told
So watch out at night or he may give you a fright!

Archie Tutt (7)
New Milton Junior School, New Milton

Hiding In A Secret Place

Hiding in a scary space
Hiding in a secret place
Out comes a creepy monster
As scary as can be
Every night, walking about
Talking to himself
Then one day, the family found
The killer of cuteness strolling about
He was scary, ugly and very slimy
Suddenly, the family had a brilliant idea
They were going to get him out of their house!

Harry Ward (7)
New Milton Junior School, New Milton

Booger

He's gross, he's green, he's sticky
He's a booger monster

I found him in my sugar
Mum plopped him in her coffee
It made it all frothy

She pulled it out, it felt like slime
It fell out of her hand
It fell on the sand
The sea took it away
I never saw my booger monster again.

George Foy (8)
New Milton Junior School, New Milton

Stalker

He stalks you in the day
He hunts you through the night
Only his patience keeps him at bay
He sneaks around like a secret spy
And he eats a lot of pie
He creeps around at night
After a month or so, you'll be in for a fright
So don't turn off the light
"Boo!"

Jamie Bell (10)
New Milton Junior School, New Milton

My Own Little Monster

Do monsters exist and are they all hairy?
Do monsters exist and are they all scary?
If monsters exist and I'm sure that they could
Are they all naughty or might some be good?
One little monster is part of my family
She's my little sister and her name is Amelie.

Aimee Louise Yeatman (8)
New Milton Junior School, New Milton

Howl

He's short and fat
His ears go floppy
Whenever he hears a howling cat

His body's spotty with poisonous warts
Bumpy, scaly horn on top
Catching mice, he just won't stop
Howling all night and all day long
To make his humble song.

Poppy Rickman (8)
New Milton Junior School, New Milton

The Slime Monster Is Under My Bed!

As suspicious as an agent
As slimy as a slug
He roams through the eerie night
Waiting for your snores
Make sure he doesn't hear you
Make sure he doesn't see you
Get under your covers
Don't make a sound
He's coming right now!

Amelia Veluthedathu (8)
New Milton Junior School, New Milton

Agro The Monster

She lurks at night looking for children who are
ungrateful
She looks for children that do not eat properly
Make sure you eat properly
And are grateful for what you have
If not, Agro the monster will come and eat you up
like a chicken.

Dexter Macklin-Palmer (9)
New Milton Junior School, New Milton

My Monster Friends

"Ssh! My monster friends and I
Are playing hide-and-seek
Bang!
Did you hear that?
It came from under the bed
Snot, that's not a good space!"

Snot is a green monster
As you can see
He is not a good hider
He is my monster friend
He also helps me mend things
With his slimy hands

Fungus is also my monster friend
He is very humongous
He is half-horse and half-alien

Sticky is very milky
But he loves dangling
But still laughing
Sticky is my favourite monster

Because he loves dancing and singing
Just like I do.

Naomi Smith (9)
North Walsall Primary Academy, Walsall

The Mean Monster

Monster, monster, could it be?
Is it here to scare me?
Is it big? Is it red?
Could it be underneath my bed?

It's fat and ugly
Dirty and grubby
Got spots everywhere
And doesn't like to share

Monster, monster, could it be?
Is it here to scare me?
Is it big? Is it red?
Could it be underneath my bed?

He's short and hairy
Weird and scary
He has small lips
And big hips

Monster, monster, could it be?
Is it here to scare me?

Is it big? Is it red?
Could it be underneath my bed?

Eliza Akhtar (9)

North Walsall Primary Academy, Walsall

Horrible Gooey Sticky-Pods

My monster is Horrible Gooey Sticky-Pods
Everywhere he sticks to things
When he sticks, the door tricks
My monster is as tall as he is wide
My monster is friendly
My monster eats Monster Munch
When he munches, he crunches his teeth
My monster likes knitting
My monster knitted a woolly jumper
He jumps and bumps
My monster plays hide-and-seek
If he finds you, he will speak
My monster has a large TV in his cave
In his cave, he has a rave.

Adam Gore (9)
North Walsall Primary Academy, Walsall

The Monster I Dare Is Everywhere

I see him in my shed
I hear him under my bed
One day, I saw him
And he was big and red
He was chubby and wrinkly
But one day, he said
"Do you want to play?"
"No! Go away!"
"Fine, I was going to go either way."
"Now, go away." That was my dare
"Fine, just remember, I'm everywhere!"

Amy Bains (10)
North Walsall Primary Academy, Walsall

Bad Boo

Boo is my name
I like to hide and shout 'boo'
Naughty or nice, I don't care
Children are what I like to scare
In cobwebs, I like to hide
I go into bins
Waiting to shout boo

They scream and squeal
As they run away
I shout boo and growl and snarl
Here I come to scare
Come to give you a giant scare.

Maimoona Bibi (7)
North Walsall Primary Academy, Walsall

Oscar The Monster

Oscar the monster
Who looked like a lobster
Was peeking through the trees
As leaves were rustling by his knees
He began to stamp and stride
And ended up on a wagon ride
The wagon stopped suddenly
Then Oscar felt shuddery
He himself became quite scared
As a boy dared to be paired
With Oscar like a lobster.

Harrison Russell-Giles (9)
North Walsall Primary Academy, Walsall

Daisy Rose The Trouble-Shooter

Daisy Rose is a kind-hearted monster
Looking for children to help
Especially children in distress
And other vulnerable people
Shape-shifter she is
Changing her physical form
To suit every situation
Making people be at peace
With one another
A trouble-shooter she is.

Princess Olamide Lawal (8)

North Walsall Primary Academy, Walsall

Crazy Daisy Monster

There is a monster under my bed
Who is crazy like a daisy
He has big, sharp fangs and likes to boogie
He is hairy like Mary, scary as Barry
He's got big, green eyes that are rounder than
peas
He runs around crazily so I named him Daisy
My crazy Daisy monster.

Bilal Muhammed (8)
North Walsall Primary Academy, Walsall

I Saw A Monster

One dark night
I saw a monster that gave me a fright
Finally, I got home
And I realised I was alone
And then I heard banging on the door
And banging on the door
I could not ignore
Then I opened the door
"Argh! There's a monster!"

Evie Grace Westley (9)
North Walsall Primary Academy, Walsall

The Monster

My monster has got four eyes
With a hairy back
And he likes to eat humans too
He is afraid of a volcano erupting
He doesn't like heights
And he has a spot on his back
Peter doesn't like to see dogs or any animal!

Safaa Hussain (7)
North Walsall Primary Academy, Walsall

The Naughty Monster

The monster wakes up at night
Will he steal something? He might
He started crawling
He saw a cake and then started drooling
But it was too late to eat the cake
The owners woke up
Now it is time for Nothy to load up.

Mariam Shahzad (8)
North Walsall Primary Academy, Walsall

The Monster

The Bogeyman and his friend play hide-and-seek
They couldn't find him
The cake came because it was his birthday
They ate the cake
And then they went to sleep
Because they were tired.

Ghulam Mustafa (7)
North Walsall Primary Academy, Walsall

Hairy Beast

This is a hairy, scary beast
This is a hairy, scary, scruffy, beast
This is a hairy, scary, scruffy, fluffy beast
This is a hairy, scary, scruffy, fluffy, pink beast
It scared me to death!

Zakiyah Ahmed (7)
North Walsall Primary Academy, Walsall

Shila The Monster

I can hear a red monster under my bed
I can hear monsters giggling under my bed
I can hear snoring under my bed
I can see red monsters under my bed.

Safa Emaan Arif (9)

North Walsall Primary Academy, Walsall

The Monster Army

My monster's name is Slimy
And he is very tiny
And he is very spiky
He looks ninety
Which is very unlikely.

Callum-James Tolley (7)
North Walsall Primary Academy, Walsall

Bake The Firetastic Monster

There once was a monster called Blake
Who lived in a large chocolate cake
He pounced around
And fell to the ground
That silly old monster called Blake!

Jacob Key (7)
Sacriston Primary School, Sacriston

Make The Monster

There once was a monster called Make
Who lived on a white icing cake
He put on his boot
And shot down the chute
That sweet, tasty monster called Make!

Warren Albert Rowbury (7)
Sacriston Primary School, Sacriston

Bendy Lead

There once was a monster called Lead
Whose nose was the size of a bead
It popped off one day
And rolled away
That blood-covered monster called Lead.

Ryan Pallister (7)
Sacriston Primary School, Sacriston

The Mystery

There once was a monster called Bat
Who liked to eat a juicy rat
He fell asleep in a heap
With a herd of sheep
That sleepy old monster called Bat!

Harvey Berry (7)
Sacriston Primary School, Sacriston

Dart's Heart

There once was a monster called Dart
Who lived in a large, beating heart
He rolled on his bed
And hit his head
That crazy old monster called Dart!

Oliver David Winn (7)
Sacriston Primary School, Sacriston

Jack And The Silly Old Sack

There once was a monster called Jack
Who lived in a silly old sack
With a little old man
Who was called Happy Dan
Who hurt his teeny weeny back!

Thomas Davidson (8)
Sacriston Primary School, Sacriston

Lead The Diver

There once was a monster called Lead
Who slept in a humongous bed
He liked to eat cake
And dive in a lake
That soggy old monster called Lead.

Jaydan James Musgrove (7)
Sacriston Primary School, Sacriston

Cakey Pakey

There once was a monster called Pake
Who lived in a very big cake
He ate a snail
And fell into a pail
What a daft old monster called Pake!

Charlie Atkinson (7)
Sacriston Primary School, Sacriston

The Cute Sneaky Boo!

Boo's tummy doesn't rumble
It'll get a little fright
Her tummy only rumbles once a year at night
Boo's horns are as sharp as her wings
But she will zoom at midnight
She'll sneak out of your house
If she's your pet, she'll escape at night
She has so many transformations
One of them is sneaky
One of them will give you a fright
Loads of them are fluffy
She is a fashion queen
She is fancy and clean
She cleans up loads of bacterial bugs
She doesn't clean up one percent of bugs
Or she'll get a fright
She's fast and no one can beat her
She's using her wing but she's the fast one.

Hannah Miller (7)
St Bernadette's RC Primary School, Whitefield

Spiker The Monster!

Spiker the monster
How short, spiky, mean and scary
He is scarier than the rest
Spiker the monster
How very snake-like
Spiker the monster never has haircuts
Haircuts just aren't his thing
Spiker the monster always hissing
Rumbling and roaring like a lion
Spiker the monster
Pretends his favourite cake
Is spider cake
But his favourite cake
Is truly cobweb cake
Spiker the monster
Spiker than the rest
Spiker the monster
Shorter than the rest
Spiker the monster
Meaner than the rest
Although he does try his hardest

To be kinder than the rest
But he just can't be kind
When someone spots him
They run away before Spiker the monster
Can even open his mouth
Would you be friends with my monster
Because, right now, he is lonely
If you be his friend
That would make me, you
And Spiker the monster very happy too!

Oscar Morton (8)
St Bernadette's RC Primary School, Whitefield

Spiky

I hear a bang in my bedroom
It is getting closer
I am scared
I can hear my monster fly over my body
I put my quilt on me
The monster got my quilt
But I was under my bed
They couldn't find me
But I accidentally made a bang
They heard it and saw me
I went downstairs
I told my mum and dad
They said, "Why are you going downstairs?"
I said, "There are monsters in my bedroom!"
They said, "Okay, you can stay down here
For one hour."
Suddenly, the monster came downstairs
My mum and dad left.

Jack Barrow (7)
St Bernadette's RC Primary School, Whitefield

Destructive Commotion

When you touch Commotion
You feel the scales running down his body
As you smell the smell of sick
As soon as you enter his cave
You hear all his snores
You hear Commotion's roar as soon as he wakes
from sleep
Commotion has an appetite like a million ravenous
lions
Wanting all the meat they could ask for
His dribble is like drips of rain dropping from the
sky
The moment people see what a destructive
creature this is
They let out a humungous cry
Everywhere Commotion roams, he leaves the smell
of sickness
What will this creature do next?

Jessica B (8)
St Bernadette's RC Primary School, Whitefield

The Eating Blob

Have you ever wondered what all the slimy trails
are in your house,
Then let me tell you... it's the Eating Blob!

The Eating Blob leaves a slimy trail wherever he
goes.
He is as slimy as a slug and as hungry as a horse.
He's circular and bounces around houses eating
everything in sight.

The Eating Blob is always hungry or is greedy!
The Blob has two tiny eyes to see and one large
one to hunt for food.
He crunches and munches his way through
everything in his path!
So hang on to your belongings because the Eating
Blob will eat them!

Louis O'Donnell (8)
St Bernadette's RC Primary School, Whitefield

Milo Monster

This is Milo Monster
His body is half-oval
He has three eyes and one will sigh
It has four horns
Two spiky and two sharp
His arms were as long as one metre
He likes to play
His horns are orange and purple
He has three legs
His tail runs down his back with red spikes
Don't mess with him
Don't be scared
There's nothing to fear
His tummy rumbled like thunder
He was as hungry as a shark
Be kind
Don't hurt him or be mean
He is a very lonely monster

Will you be his friend?

Zak Wegg (8)
St Bernadette's RC Primary School, Whitefield

Fluffy The Cutest Monster Around

She is as cute as a newborn baby and is a very gentle, small monster
Fluffy is as cute as a bunny and is beautiful inside
Fluffy hates people being mean, it can't resist so it will tear them apart
For some reason, she can fly and can speak all animal languages
She smells like doughnuts and lavender
She is as small as a mouse
And she is so good
That you would go to sleep or feel hungry
Whenever they are gone
That is when she is flying
When she's blue, she's sad
And wants lots of love and doughnuts.

Gracie B (8)
St Bernadette's RC Primary School, Whitefield

Ripley The Monster

He is always really lonely
He is always hungry, but he gets full
His teeth are always wobbly from chewing the
meat
He creeps up the streets for food to eat
He eats everything in his path
Children to adults, he always looks for his dinner
If the lights are on and you're in bed
When you wake up, you'll be in his tummy
When you go to bed, turn the lights off
And you will be safe
When it's daytime, don't look down the drain
Or you'll be in his jaws
Will you be his friend?

Luke Ryan (8)
St Bernadette's RC Primary School, Whitefield

Milo Monster

This is Milo Monster
He's the best
Don't go to him
He is as hungry as ten big dinos
Don't mess with him
He's as fierce as 100,000 sharks
His tail is ragged and sharp like a knife
Don't mess, he is as sharp and tall as a T-rex
His foot is the size of an enormous limo
Don't look if you don't wear sunglasses
Do not mess with him or it will be your last
His claws and his teeth make it easier to crunch
The mothers and children he will have for lunch.

George Badlan (8)
St Bernadette's RC Primary School, Whitefield

Dag, The Dangerous Dragon

Out on the lake, a lovely day
Nobody knows that danger is at bay
Underneath the surface lives a dangerous creature
He glides through the water, swishing his tail, his favourite creature
Stretching out his shady tentacles looking for food
He's a dangerous dude!

Look out! Beware
Who goes there?
Don't go in the water
You really shouldn't oughta
It's dangerous Dag
He will shake you like a log
You will be dead and go to hospital in a bag!

James Simpson (7)
St Bernadette's RC Primary School, Whitefield

I Am Bonkers Boniflebick

I am Bonkers Boniflebick
I'm absolutely humongous
I roam around my valley
Including all the alleys.
The spiky, wet antennas on my head
Helps me to see food and predators
From far away.
They keep me very safe and healthy
My antennae smell of the sewers
They also taste of sick
They make a lot of noise
And sometimes even click.
I am as spiky as a shark's fin
I weigh as much as four elephants
And have spikes coming out of my chin.

Ethan Brower (8)
St Bernadette's RC Primary School, Whitefield

Super Blob

He is really friendly
He is cuter than a bunny
And he's a superhero
He's more powerful
Than a huge, hard bulldozer
He has purple, strange spots
All over his spiky back
He has lots of eyes on his slimy face
And some on his antennae
So he can see food from a distance
He can fly, so when he sees it with his eyes
He can fly over to the food
Super Blob has claws as sharp as lion's teeth
When he walks, he makes the earth wobble.

Freddie Mollard (8)
St Bernadette's RC Primary School, Whitefield

Crogon

If you feel the ground shake or get poked
It might be Crogon's wrecking ball
Crogon smells like blood
His claws are as sharp as daggers
He is as big as three double-decker buses
Stacked on top of each other
He can shrink to be as small as a lizard
Crogon's teeth drip with blood
Crogon is as mischievous as a monkey
His teeth are like thousands of swords
Crogon's tummy rumbles like thunder
His wrecking ball swishes past like a bird.

Tom Dalton (8)
St Bernadette's RC Primary School, Whitefield

Burn

He smells like he's eaten pancakes
His tummy rumbles like a thunderous cloud
His body parts are like magma
He is as cheeky as a monkey
His bottomless tummy is like the whole world
His fire burns like a sword
His face is the shape of fire
He is always hungry like he hasn't eaten in years
His stripes are made out of lava
He is as giant as a tree
His body can pounce as high as the almighty
Mount Everest.

Donatas S (8)
St Bernadette's RC Primary School, Whitefield

The Woolly Cuddly

Woolly Cuddly sounds like a very shy lamb
When he laughs, it echoes loudly
Because his stomach is empty
When he walks, it sounds like a little sugar plum
fairy
Tip-toeing down the stairs.

His voice sounds like tiny bells jingling
When he tries to communicate with people
All anyone hears is a quiet, "Babababa!"
When Woolly eats, it sounds like a cat peacefully
purring.
We love you, Woolly Cuddly.

Grace Hadman (9)
St Bernadette's RC Primary School, Whitefield

Air

I can hear wind whooshing
Blowing through my hair
I feel monsters watching
I see one too
My friend monster flies through the window
With its wings stroking my ear
Feet scraping on the road
Knees as bendy as a band
Air's wings are fluffy and spotty
Eyes as bright as the full moon
Wait, shh for a second
Now we have finished
Let me say goodnight
And don't let the bed bugs bite.

Mia Rose Williams (7)
St Bernadette's RC Primary School, Whitefield

The Monster

I can hear a monster growling through the streets
As vicious as a lion
There is slime all over the streets
He is cheeky like a monkey
He is spotty like a leopard
Slimier and goopier than glue
And he loves to eat glowing things
But he loves to eat people
At night, get under your covers
Don't make a peep
In the morning, he will be gone
Will you be there
Or will you be gone?

Martha Lily Tait (7)
St Bernadette's RC Primary School, Whitefield

Slimy The Hungry Monster

Slimy the hungry monster
Slimy zoomed like a rocket into the shop
She got all the slime and fluff in the shop
And ate it all up
Slimy has a glistening, purple headband
With a beautiful flower
Her slime is as green as a snail
Slimy is half slimy and half fluffy
Slimy is as hungry as a lion
Slimy is friendly like being your best friend
How would you be if you were an alien?

Freya Linaker (7)
St Bernadette's RC Primary School, Whitefield

I Am Thinking Of A Monster Called Hot Waffle

I can smell the smell of a waffle monster
I am thinking that he's long and furry
His long tail goes up to his shiny, yellow crown
I can hear him roaring like the biggest car engine
in the universe
Then, out of the darkness
I see a red and orange monster
But, when he saw me
He went back under the bed like a terrifying lion
I wonder what monster is waiting for you under the
bed?

Madeleine Ohamara (7)

St Bernadette's RC Primary School, Whitefield

The Monster And The Giant

He is as giant as a martian
He always flies when he has cake
Chicken, chips and ice cream
His skin looks like glowing, green slime
Everywhere he flies, his slime falls off
Every time his belly rumbles, it feels like slime
He can hear everything with his giant ears
He is cheekier than a monkey
He is hairy like a gorilla
He is tall like a zebra in a tree.

Luca Bailey (8)
St Bernadette's RC Primary School, Whitefield

The Monster Who Shape-Shifts Is...

All over Dier's body are very dangerous
Spikes that are very poisonous
As Dier walks around, he makes a trail of
chocolate
Dier can be as hungry as a pack of lions put
together
He can shape-shift into anything in the world
As Dier was having a fly round
He zoomed past everyone in the town
Sometimes, Dier's belly rumbles so much, it sounds
like a T-rex.

Charlie N (8)
St Bernadette's RC Primary School, Whitefield

Sad Sid

He is generally sad
His head is bright
Most of the time
He laughs
He likes to play in the rain
But then he's sad
So he needs a cheer
When he gets mad
He is as funny as a chimpanzee
But what causes that?
His eyes are as devilish
As the Bermuda Triangle
So now, read the question
Are you sure you'll have a PvP with him?

Daniel Yusuf Patelmama (9)
St Bernadette's RC Primary School, Whitefield

Slimy Princess

I can feel her slimy slime, Slimy Princess roars like mad.
As quick as a flash, the slime travels down her back, her antenna's smell like mouldy garlic bread.
It's antenna's are as thin as a pencil.
I can hear her heavy breathing slowly moving through the air at night.
Slimy Princess is always changing her ways,
My monster is tamed like a good day.

Ella F (8)
St Bernadette's RC Primary School, Whitefield

Friendly Spotty

Friendly Spotty has horns as big as two bulls
Her tummy rumbles like thunder when she gets
hungry
She likes to play, she would play all day if she
could
Spotty could fly to the moon and back
In one minute with her flowery wings
Her body is as spotty as a young stingray
Her face is definitely as cute as a puppy
Would you like her as a pet?

Charlotte May Griffiths (8)
St Bernadette's RC Primary School, Whitefield

Fluffy The Friendly, Cute Cloud!

This is Fluffy
The friendly, cute cloud
Fluffy is as cute as a newborn baby
And is as small as a baby rabbit
Fluffy goes, *hehe! Haha!*
When something is funny
She goes *lala!* when she is happy
As she floats across the ground
She leaves small pieces of cloud
Trailing behind her

Will you be her friend?

Erin Katie Eckersley (8)
St Bernadette's RC Primary School, Whitefield

The Poem About Me, Venom

I'm as hungry as one thousand robust wolves
Everywhere I roam, I leave human-sized, black and slimy, loud footsteps
My claws are as strong as a robust wolf's bite
My tummy is like a never-ending, thundering pit
I have spikes that are as sharp as a megalodon's teeth
I'm robust, more terrifying than an orange lion.

Zack Cooper-Gibb (8)
St Bernadette's RC Primary School, Whitefield

The Footsteps

I was in my bed, going to sleep
I heard footsteps
I jumped out of my bed
I was scared
I crept out of bed
I ran downstairs
And I saw a monster
I ran back upstairs
I grabbed Dolly
And hid under my bed
I peeped out
I could see the monster
I stopped peeping
And realised monsters are friendly!

Isabella Jane Jones (7)
St Bernadette's RC Primary School, Whitefield

The Monster

The monster is
As spotty as a football
Greedy as a venom bear
His teeth are as sharp as a dragon
When he goes for a walk, he finds a smell of cake
His tail is as spiky as a cactus
When he goes outside
He is as tall as a house
He is a cute, soft monster
He is a bit small
He has weird-looking, furry hair.

Heidi Betty Mullen (8)
St Bernadette's RC Primary School, Whitefield

Fluff Monster

I can hear a monster growling underneath my bed
His name is Fluffy Fred
His fluffy, soft tail is jolly and gentle
His claws and his teeth make it easy to crunch
The cupcakes and biscuits he'll have for his lunch
So if there's a monster underneath your bed
Don't fight it off
Because it could be Fluffy Fred!

Nell Redmond (8)
St Bernadette's RC Primary School, Whitefield

The Spiky Monster

There is a monster called Kitty
Kitty is fluffy on her tummy
Her tummy is a pink colour
She is as spotty as a leopard
Kitty is very shy
Kitty stomped like a stamping crocodile to the shop
Kitty is a playful, excited pup
Do you think Kitty is excited to have a friend?
Kitty is a playful monster.

Shannon Costello (7)
St Bernadette's RC Primary School, Whitefield

Sicky Gorgon

He feels like furry, fluffy hair
Sicky is as spiky as a cactus
He is as hungry as a ravenous lion
He smells like sausages
So everywhere he goes
It smells like sausages
Sicky Gorgon is a lonely but friendly monster
When he touches stuff
He can only feel sausages
He roams around everywhere.

James K (8)
St Bernadette's RC Primary School, Whitefield

The Monster Who Flies Is...

As mischievous as a hungry monkey
His wings can glide past the Leaning Tower of Pisa
Its rock-hard wings have spikes all down them
His smooth antlers catch rain that he drinks from
The beast's four eyes can let him spot food better
And his speed can beat a Peregrin falcon
He is as spiky as a dagger.

Theo H (8)

St Bernadette's RC Primary School, Whitefield

Fiery Brian

Meet Brian
You might think Brian is just an ordinary monster
Oh no
You have just made a big mistake
Brian is a bloodthirsty monster
Don't get tricked by his cuteness
Because he will rip you in half
Beware, Brian
Might be under your bed tonight

Will you be the unlucky one?

Cole Green (9)
St Bernadette's RC Primary School, Whitefield

King Horzel

He smells like some delicious cake
It is as big as a spinosaurus
He is as hungry as a pack of megalodons
He is a very gentle giant
Its skin is brighter than the sun
He has a colossal sense of smell
He has a great sense of taste
His skin is really hard and soft
Really soft actually.

Finley Mountford (8)
St Bernadette's RC Primary School, Whitefield

Axell's Amazing Poem

Axell is a wonderfully strange monster
If he goes touched, he glows a magical, dark red
His cheeky imagination means Axel can do
whatever he wants
And whatever he wishes for

He is a kind monster that can show or do anything
just for you
Axell's blue boosters spark like a burning flame.

Aidan Lewis (8)
St Bernadette's RC Primary School, Whitefield

Slopy Slapy

When Slapy gets to hear you
He will slowly creep up on you
Leaving a poisonous trail behind you
But when you look around
He's gone in a *poof*
But, when he does get to you
He will slap you with his poisonous spikes
And you will start levitating in the air
Flying away...

Robert Zakrzewski (8)
St Bernadette's RC Primary School, Whitefield

The Monster Who Is Smelly Is...

George is the smelliest monster on Earth
His hair is as spiky as a cactus
His stomach rumbled so he ate his burger
When he gets angry, he roars as loud as a
dinosaur's roar
He is really great to have as a friend
He is cool and nice
He is normal kid-size
He looks really cute.

Grace Emily Weber (8)
St Bernadette's RC Primary School, Whitefield

Scary's House

Scary likes my diary
Who's as white as snow
Scary is a superhero
Scary yells when fairies hit his toe
Scary destroys the fairies
Scary is now sad about the fairies
Scary's teeth are spiky like dinosaurs'
Now no one goes near him
Would you go near him?

Harry Marshall (7)
St Bernadette's RC Primary School, Whitefield

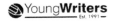

Tupac

Tupac smells like rotten eggs and he is as lonely as a pony
He's got eight eyes and eight legs
So he is an arachnid.
His eyes help him find his prey easily
His short legs help him scatter around the floor
Be wary as he's scary and he might be behind your bedroom door.

Zak Zain Crampton (8)

St Bernadette's RC Primary School, Whitefield

Small But Spectacular Bongy

His fork-shaped head feels as hot as a pan
A huge whiff of soil hits your nostrils
His handle was as long as a giraffe's neck
Bongy's fork-like body is similar to a real one
Bongy zipped into micro-size
Now he's as small as a nit
He got planted into a chip!

Teddy Langston C (8)
St Bernadette's RC Primary School, Whitefield

The Cuddle Team Leader

I can hear the Cuddle Team Leader
Growling in the street
I get under the covers
If he spots me, I will be stuck in his jaws
He is as nasty as a witch
When the Cuddle Team Leader
Smashes his tongue against the ground
It knocks down all the buildings in the world.

Callum John Kirby (7)
St Bernadette's RC Primary School, Whitefield

Gruffles The Friendly Monster

He's as pink as a bag of candyfloss
As fluffy as a brand new teddy
Every night, he wakes up to see the nice sunset
He's as cute as a newborn kitten
And he's as friendly as a new pet
But he is never given pancakes
Will you give him pancakes?

Ronnie Knowles (8)
St Bernadette's RC Primary School, Whitefield

The Destroyer

The Destroyer is even more destructive than three thousand bombs
His fangs feel so sharp that you would think they could cut through metal
He dashes through the villages, stealing all the food
If he wasn't in a cage, he would cause a lot of destruction.

Thomas Hugh Colohan (8)
St Bernadette's RC Primary School, Whitefield

Hungry Zak

This is Hungry Zak
He's as happy as a pet
He's as lonely as something in a cage
He's as loving as a cat, dog or hamster
He's as fluffy as a fluffy dog
He's as cute as the cutest thing in the world
Will you be his friend?

Aidan Simmonds (8)
St Bernadette's RC Primary School, Whitefield

Bug And The Great Big Duck

He can eat you faster than a cheetah can run
His fur is as rough as a spider's hair
He is as dangerous as a ferocious shark
His name is Bug
He eats your chickens
So, at night, hide your farm animals
Because the vicious Bug is out there.

Sam Hopkins (7)
St Bernadette's RC Primary School, Whitefield

This Is Stampy

This is Stampy
Fluffy and cute
He is as hairy as a lion's mane
Big, friendly giant
Thud, thud, thud
Stampy stomps and makes the ground shake
Massive horns
He likes to taste rough and sharp pencils
Will you hug him?

Ciaran Howe (8)
St Bernadette's RC Primary School, Whitefield

Star's Poem

Meet Star
Star is cute but naughty
She is so fluffy, just like a puppy
Sometimes, she is as scared as a rabbit
So she needs a friend
Because she's lonely
She is kind and gentle and also honest
Will you be her friend?

Stella Chan (8)
St Bernadette's RC Primary School, Whitefield

The Flying Monster Being Evil

The flying monster was eating people's food
When people go to bed, they see footsteps
The flying monster loves metal more than
everything in the whole world
And he likes wood in the world
And some prickly horns in the world.

Maximilian Holt (7)
St Bernadette's RC Primary School, Whitefield

He

He is a scary monster that lives in the forest
His back is as spiky as a lion's mane
He's got humongous nails with spots on them
He has got a very long tongue
His belly rumbles like a thunderstorm.

Olivia W (8)
St Bernadette's RC Primary School, Whitefield

Bogey Brain

He smells like rotten cheese
His body is spikier than sharp teeth
His mouth is as slimy as a super gooey bogey
Monster X shakes like crazy
Will you be his friend?
Monster X is the best.

Ryan Firth (8)
St Bernadette's RC Primary School, Whitefield

Michael

His body feels like a lizard
His body smells like crystal slime
His spikes are as warm as the sun
He is as big as a tower
And it is as sharp as a trap.

Kian F (8)
St Bernadette's RC Primary School, Whitefield

Me And The Evil Monster

He was stinky like a hairy wolf
Sticky's hair swished as he moved along
He was as big as an elephant
His hands were covered with purple spots.

Keane Forshaw (8)
St Bernadette's RC Primary School, Whitefield

Slappy Haunted House

Slappy is scary
With fire on his head
He has a welly on his belly
He has sharp teeth like rocks
Slappy has a gigantic mouth.

Aven James Wallsworth (7)
St Bernadette's RC Primary School, Whitefield

Mr Marley

Mr Marley is full of snot
It drips out of his nose a lot
It is a lovely shade of green
It is the drippiest of the lot.

Leo
St Bernadette's RC Primary School, Whitefield

Cross Pinky

Cross Pinky came stomping, stomping, stomping
Cross Pinky came stomping, stomping, stomping
up to the old wine store

He looks like a slimy slug
And moves like a wobbly jelly
His belly is pink like a pig's
And his idea of sport is watching the telly

Cross Pinky came stomping, stomping, stomping
Cross Pinky came stomping, stomping, stomping
up to the old wine store

His eyes are as round as ping pong balls
His voice is deep like a whale
He likes to wear pink jumpers
And drinks lots of ale

Cross Pinky came stomping, stomping, stomping
Cross Pinky came stomping, stomping, stomping
up to the old wine store

When he is not drinking
He will go on a boat and sail

But, when he is blind drunk
He needs to read the drink's menu in braille

Cross Pinky came stomping, stomping, stomping
Cross Pinky came stomping, stomping, stomping
Away from the old wine store.

Archie Sinclair Willis (10)
St Mary's CE (VC) J&I School, Sowerby Bridge

Broccoli

Broccoli came jumping, jumping, jumping
Broccoli came jumping, jumping, jumping to the
cinema door

He has spiky teeth
And broccoli hair
And his bones are on the outside
His ears like oak leaves
And he is incredible to hide

Broccoli came jumping, jumping, jumping
Broccoli came jumping, jumping, jumping to the
cinema door

With a handful of salted popcorn
Shoved into his face
He came running, running, running
Like he was in a 100-metre race

Broccoli came jumping, jumping, jumping
Broccoli came jumping, jumping, jumping to the
cinema door

He shoved his mouth full of meat

He regurgitated down his juice
He'd forgotten to eat his greens
So his bowels came loose

Broccoli came jumping, jumping, jumping
Broccoli came jumping, jumping, jumping to the
bathroom door!

Arron Lapsley (10)

St Mary's CE (VC) J&I School, Sowerby Bridge

Crumble

His face was like a potato
His nose was flat as a floor
His fingers were as small as rice
His favourite thing was the sweet store

Crumble came bouncing, bouncing, bouncing
Crumble came bouncing up to your garden lawn

His body was as big as his sweet stash
His ears were like tennis balls
His arms were as tiny as mice
Watch out, you'll find him in walls

Crumble came bouncing, bouncing, bouncing
Crumble came bouncing up to your front door

In the light, he is dreadfully cute
But be wary
In the dead of night
He is very scary

Crumble came bouncing, bouncing, bouncing
Crumble came bouncing up to your bedroom door!

Lily Reynolds Norman (10)
St Mary's CE (VC) J&I School, Sowerby Bridge

Banna

Banna came bouncing, bouncing, bouncing
Banna came bouncing up to the old market store

Hair like slime of a slug
A nose like an apple core
Eyes like fluffy scrunchies
And lips covered in gore

Banna came bouncing, bouncing, bouncing
Banna came bouncing up to the old market store

Skin like yellow lemons
Eyes as bright as the sun
He wears a hat of loneliness
And never seems to have fun

Banna came bouncing, bouncing, bouncing
Banna came bouncing up to the old market store

He waddles around
Like a sad, lonely nana
Wishing his life
Was happy like a llama

Lucia Filomena Wilson Pignataro (10)
St Mary's CE (VC) J&I School, Sowerby Bridge

Sam The Whinger

His skin was soft and bony
His eyes were as brown as dirt
His breath smelt like a ditch
And all he did was flirt

Sam came sprinting, sprinting, sprinting
Sam came sprinting, sprinting, sprinting
Up to the stadium pitch

Big and tall, he stood
Huge horns upon his head
His voice was loud and deep
And he loved to eat some bread

Sam came sprinting, sprinting, sprinting
Sam came sprinting, sprinting, sprinting
Up to the stadium pitch

He was a football full of naughtiness
As fast as an assassin ninja
His voice was like a chicken
And he was a total whinger.

Arthur Beddoe (10)
St Mary's CE (VC) J&I School, Sowerby Bridge

Blob

His teeth were as blunt as classroom scissors
His hair all scuffled and smelly
His eyes were brown and dog-like
With velvety marshmallows sticking out of his belly

Blob came shuffling, shuffling, shuffling
Bob came shuffling, shuffling, shuffling up to the
old see-saw

His fur, all dog-like and shaggy
His eyes the size of bin lids
His feet small and bony
Smaller than a billy goat's kids

Bob went shuffling, shuffling, shuffling
Bob went shuffling, shuffling, shuffling
Away from the old see-saw.

Maia Wood (10)
St Mary's CE (VC) J&I School, Sowerby Bridge

Noodles

When walking in the dark
You might see
My good friend Noodles
Eating KFC
He's very, very naughty
And likes to pull pranks
He's utterly kind
Although he never says thanks
Sassy and cute
Cheeky and fat
My friend Noodles
Is all of that
Even though he never says thanks
Noodles has two very best friends
Who will still like him even when the world ends
One of the friends is me
And my name is Manny
The other is an old lady
Oops! She's my granny
Noodles is really
An awesome friend

And I will stay with him
Right to the end.

Jude Blackburn (10)
St Mary's CE (VC) J&I School, Sowerby Bridge

Nugget Bugget

Her eyes were fresh green peas
She had a face like fish batter
Her knees were bumpy and lumpy
But to her, it didn't matter

Nugget came waddling
Waddling
Waddling
Up to McDonald's glass door

Her arms were wiggly worms
Her legs were short and stubby
Her hair like burnt spaghetti
Her belly amazingly chubby

Nugget came waddling
Waddling
Waddling
Up to McDonald's glass door

Her feet small and square
The scent strong and meaty

Her toenails raging red
From sitting on what she called a 'seaty'.

Molly Ledger (10)
St Mary's CE (VC) J&I School, Sowerby Bridge

Cal

His eyes are black
Like rubber tyres
His gasoline smells
Like moist wires

Cal came crunching, crunching, crunching
Cal came crunching
Up to Toronto Towers

He used all his power
To destroy the city
He smashed up the Tower
Which was a pity

Cal came crunching, crunching, crunching
Cal came crunching
Up to Toronto Towers

He realised he had done
Something wrong
By wrecking the towers
Now he had nowhere to belong

Cal came crunching, crunching, crunching
Cal came crunching
Away from Toronto Towers.

Beck Jameson (10)
St Mary's CE (VC) J&I School, Sowerby Bridge

The Hairy, Scary Monster

The hairy, scary monster
Wanders around the city
Be careful or he'll scare you
And the sight will not be pretty

He taps your back
And cries out, "Boo!"
Then puts his filthy hands on you

His spikes are as sharp as shark's teeth
His hair is mouldy straw
His clothes are old and tattered
And his voice is an evil roar

If you come across this vile beast
There's only one thing to do
Insult his dirty, tangled hair
And he'll never come back for you.

Chloe Davies (10)
St Mary's CE (VC) J&I School, Sowerby Bridge

Gurgle

Gurgle was covered in long, pink fur
Blue spots on his back in a line
Hunched over, always looking at the floor
Twisting and curling up his spine

His small, chubby legs were flaky
And disgusting toenails on his feet
Teeth that could tear you in seconds
Someone you never want to meet

His face was shaped like a huge egg
His great eye the colour of green
Two horrible horns by the side of his head
He might not be the worst, but he's definitely mean.

Anna Louise Walker (10)
St Mary's CE (VC) J&I School, Sowerby Bridge

Susie Salt

Her voice is deep
Her eyes are peas
She is so small
And loves to play in leaves

Her nose is small and stumpy
Her feet are long and skinny
Her hands are big and green
Her heart is shaped like mine

Bananas grow out of her ears
She has fruit as her hair
But she doesn't like it
Because it grows everywhere

Her skin is blue
And very bumpy, but
She only minds about her teeth
Being incredibly lumpy.

Ayla Amos (11)
St Mary's CE (VC) J&I School, Sowerby Bridge

Squish

His voice is sweet
His eyes are corn
He is small and chubby
And loves cutting the lawn
Squish came waddling
Waddling
Waddling
Squish came waddling
Waddling
Waddling
Waddling
To the old sweet shop door
"One bite if you dare!"
Said Squish, so
They took a bite in the dead
Of night...

Holly Jaime O'Connor (11)
St Mary's CE (VC) J&I School, Sowerby Bridge

Life Of A Firepaw

Firepaw is a half-human baby kitten in the
orphanage
She always stays in the shade
She works at a very young age
She feels like she is everyone's maid

She is the opposite of shy
In her bed, she does lie
She always wants to fly
"I want to kill," she said

Firepaw goes to kill a man
She is judged by a mouse
She leaves the house 'cause of the fan
She says, "This is a weird house."

"I'm doing the wrong thing," she whispered
She scratched the wall with her sharp claws
Firepaw and the rat bickered
She held her paws

She was followed by the police
They got their guns

I invented my peace
This was not fun

Two years later, she's sent to a family
She loves their fries
These guys have saved me
Now there are no more cries.

Eshan Kabuye (10)
St Patrick's Primary School, Glasgow

The Stalker

The Stalker hunts for his prey
The children don't see him in the night
As the children fall asleep, they bray
The monster wants to make the timing right

After they fall asleep
He quickly dives in the room
He tries not to make any noise as he sweeps
Across the room, the children don't see the doom

You hope it's a dream, but it's not
When you hear something, you wake up
But you don't see anyone, just a flowerpot
The monster makes sure he has a good lineup

He tries to make a way
To get you without a fight
He looks at your shoes coloured grey
But he sees you out of sight.

Dominykas Dankis (10)
St Patrick's Primary School, Glasgow

A Story About A Beast

A humongous beast lives on the street
If he finds you, you'll be a lovely treat
He shoots beaming-hot red lasers wherever you are
Even goes to Alaska, yes, that far

He crushes you with spikes as long as a school
Be careful, don't think he's a fool
He locks you in closets with spooky things
When he shoots slime from his arms they're just like springs

He sets buildings on fire that are worth a lot of money
When he finds you in the dark, it won't be funny
He has the ability to lift anything, cars, even a sack
But remember one thing, he will be back.

Hassan Ali Bhatti (9)
St Patrick's Primary School, Glasgow

Stella's Midnight Adventure

My monster is a teddy
She comes alive at night
She is always ready
When there's no light

My monster's really sneaky
She loves to fly and lie
But she's never sleepy
Stella can't fly high

She sneaks to the fridge for a sweet
She flies when everyone's asleep
She loves to play trick or treat
If you see her, you'll want to weep

She's lost in the house already
You will see her at first sight
Don't touch her, she'll turn deadly
And she might even bite.

Sophie Chanelle McKay (10)
St Patrick's Primary School, Glasgow

The Demonic Reaper Goes To Town

My monster likes to scare
In the middle of the night
If you play truth or dare
Then you might get a fright
He's like a spy with his three eyes at night
A sudden move makes the ground crack
The guy went to get his pills
Suddenly he saw something in the darkness
He went out to check
The Reaper makes a creepy sound
Shivers down his spine.

Mehmet Ali Kocoglu (10)

St Patrick's Primary School, Glasgow

Candy The Monster's Life

Don't go out at night
'Cause it will come and swipe you
And your chocolate at sight
And you will get a big fright
She has three arms and is white
She is hungry for sweets
But she has no sweets
If you don't give her sugar
She will bite you
Even when she will beat you
She will make you her hunter for candy.

Baillie Hutchison (9)
St Patrick's Primary School, Glasgow

The Seeker

Seeker is a friendly ghost
He likes to play hide-and-seek
And likes to seek the most
He doesn't have feet

Seeker can hide behind a flower
He can drive a car
Midnight is his favourite hour
He can fly far

He likes new friends to make
Seeker never lies
He likes to bake
And doesn't like mice.

Lenka Malgorzata (10)
St Patrick's Primary School, Glasgow

My Monster

My monster is shy
She always tells the truth as if she has a spell
When she starts to act shy, she always cries
Of course, she is adorable as well
She always loves a cuddle.

Maci McCusker (10)
St Patrick's Primary School, Glasgow

YOUNG WRITERS INFORMATION

We hope you have enjoyed reading this book – and that you will continue to in the coming years.

If you're a young writer who enjoys reading and creative writing, or the parent of an enthusiastic poet or story writer, do visit our website **www.youngwriters.co.uk**. Here you will find free competitions, workshops and games, as well as recommended reads, a poetry glossary and our blog. There's lots to keep budding writers motivated to write!

If you would like to order further copies of this book, or any of our other titles, then please give us a call or order via your online account.

Young Writers
Remus House
Coltsfoot Drive
Peterborough
PE2 9BF
(01733) 890066
info@youngwriters.co.uk

Join in the conversation!
Tips, news, giveaways and much more!

 YoungWritersUK

 @YoungWritersCW